MW00808513

★ Get Up & Go ★

*To my husband and children*
*whose boundless energy and zest for life*
*have given me wonderful reasons*
*to GET UP & GO every day*

# Get Up & Go

## Fun Ideas for Getting Fit as a Family

BY JENNIFER FLANDERS

Prescott Publishing
Tyler, Texas

Copyright © 2014, Jennifer Flanders

Cover design, interior design, and typesetting:
Jennifer Flanders


Cover photos:
Microsoft Office Stock Photos (front)
David Flanders Photography (back)

Publisher:
Prescott Publishing
3726 Woods Blvd.
Tyler, TX 75707
http://prescottpublishing.org


ISBN: 978-1-938945-07-6
LCCN: 2014913257

Unless otherwise noted, all Scripture references are taken from
THE NEW AMERICAN STANDARD BIBLE ®, Copyright
©1960, 1962, 1963, 1968, 1971, 1972, 1973, 1975, 1977, 1995 by
the Lockman Foundation. Used by permission.

The ideas and suggestions espoused in this book are not intended
as a substitute for consulting with a physician. This book is
intended as a reference volume only, not as a medical manual.
Neither the authors nor the publisher shall be liable or responsible
for any loss or damage allegedly arising from any information or
suggestion in this book. Mention of specific companies,
organizations, or authorities in this book does not imply
endorsement by the authors or publisher, nor does mention of
specific companies, organizations, or authorities imply that they
endorse this book, its authors, or the publisher.

# - CONTENTS -

## Section 1: Mark, Set, Go

## Section 2: Morning Calisthenics

## Section 3: How to Have a Ball

## Section 4: Pedal Pushers

## Section 5: Let's Play Tag

## Section 6: Chalk Up Some Fun

# Section 7: Keep Your Balance

# Section 8: Heart Healthy Housekeeping

# Section 9: Great Chores Outdoors

# Section 10: Let's Get Wet & Wild

## Section 11: Back to Nature

## Section 12: Getting Fit Out and About

## Section 13: Pool Party Games

## Section 14: Rainy Day Fun

## Section 15: Spring Training

## Section 16: Summer Sports

## Section 17: Fall Fitness

## Section 18: Winter Workouts

# - FOREWORD -

Newton's First Law of Motion states: A body at rest will continue at rest, and a body in motion will continue in motion, unless acted upon by a stronger force. This is what we call *inertia.*

It's something we can observe not only in time and space, but in families as well.

Some children are bursting with boundless energy and endless activity. Apart from prescription meds, there's no slowing them down! This book will give their weary parents fresh ideas on how to channel that energy in constructive, family-friendly ways.

Other children would be content to sit on the couch for the duration, if it meant they could keep watching television or playing video games. They are bodies at rest, and they will remain at rest until a stronger force does something about it.

Mom and Dad, *you are that force.* These sedentary children need to get up, get moving, and get their blood pumping on a regular basis. They need for you to set some boundaries, set the example, and set aside time for getting fit, together.

We live in a day and age when 75% of American youth are ineligible for military service because they are "too fat to fight." Despite the fact there are 24-hour gyms on every corner and organized sports available year-round, obesity has reached epidemic proportions.

We desperately need a new approach—an approach that makes fitness fun—and we need a way to pursue fitness that keeps the family intact.

As homeschoolers, the way our family has approached physical education has, for the most part, been extremely informal. But it is this very informality that has made it so successful.

We spend time together, we stay active, we have fun, and as an added bonus, we get some good exercise, to boot! It's as if physical fitness were a by-product of what we do, rather than the goal.

Because this kind of fitness is fun, our kids have not only embraced it enthusiastically, but have continued to pursue it into adulthood, long after they've left home.

We hope the same will be true for your family as you incorporate the ideas in this book into your daily lives.

Have fun, and God bless!
- Doug Flanders, MD

# - INTRODUCTION -

Some time ago, I received a letter from a reader that voiced a common frustration for many mothers I've met over the years—a frustration I've felt myself from time to time, especially in those bygone days when my husband and I were first beginning our family.

The letter read:

> *Dear Jennifer,*
>
> *We have five children, ranging in age from 2-11. I need to get in shape, but I can never find the time with all the kids around. Any suggestions?*
>
> *Busy Young Mom*

I need to get in shape... but I don't have the time... and my kids get in the way. Does that sound familiar?

It's easy to get in the mindset that exercise is what you do at the gym three days a week—and if you can't find a babysitter (or afford a gym membership), you're doomed to a life of dumpiness.

Nothing could be further from the truth!

As I've discovered during my quarter-century of mothering, when it comes to getting and staying in shape, we shouldn't view our children as an obstacle, but as an asset. They give us great reasons for making fitness a priority: We need to get in shape so we can take care of them. We need to stay in shape so we can keep up with them. And we need to make sure they're in shape, so they can live long, healthy, productive lives.

Working out and raising children are not mutually exclusive activities. With a little imagination and a willingness to multi-task, we can *get fit* together and have a great time doing it.

If, like the busy young mom who sent me that letter, you don't have a clue where to begin, you've come to the right place. In the pages that follow, you will find 111 tried-and-true suggestions for incorporating physical fitness into your daily routine in fun, family-friendly ways.

Give them a try, and you'll be well on the way to building stronger, healthier bodies for yourself and your children, and making lots of great memories in the process.

So, what are you waiting for? Let's get started....

## Section 1

# Mark, Set, Go!

# -1-
# Foot Races

Get ready… get set…. Few things cause our children to come running faster than the prospect of a good race.

Big ones and little ones alike love the opportunity to test their speed against brothers and sisters, neighbors and friends. All it takes is Daddy calling, "Race you home!" and an evening walk is finished in a hurry.

We'll often give the younger children a head start, although they all long for the day they won't need it. We have a few kids in our family who are especially fast, so they get challenged more than anyone else, as beating them in a foot race really *means* something.

Want to get your kids running? There's no need to head to the track. Race them to the mailbox, to the next lamppost, to that big tree at the top of the hill.

If you start when they're little, you may have to hold back a bit for them to keep up, but all too soon, they will be leaving you in the dust as they grow in stature and skill.

And that's a *good* thing!

3

# -2-
# Silly Races

Not all races are about stop watches and form and setting personal records. Don't be afraid to mix things up a bit.

Variety is the spice of life!

If your kids grow tired of plodding to the finish line, one foot in front of the other, try a couple of these variations:

- SQUATTING RACE: Bend your knees, sit on your heels, and waddle like a duck.

- WALKING RACE: Keep your legs straight and walk on your heels. Keep one foot on the ground at all times.

- SKIPPING RACE: Hop, skip, or jump to the finish line. Be sure to demonstrate the desired step!

- BACKWARD RACE: Run backwards, but watch where you're going!

- CRAWLING RACE: Race on hands and knees. Best to be indoors on the carpet for this one.

- SACK RACE: Put your feet in the sack and hop to the finish line. A pillowcase will work, too!

# -3-
# Two-Man Races

If you want to mix things up even further, grab a partner and race in teams. There are many fun ways to do this. Try one of the following ideas, and see how well you do:

• THREE-LEGGED RACE: Have partners stand next to one another, then use a bandana or a piece of rope to tie their inside legs together at the knee. Once all the teams are joined, line up and race to the finish line.

• WHEELBARROW RACE: Line up, facing the same direction. The person in front does a handstand while his partner supports his legs by holding them under his arms in the crooks of his elbows. To race, the "wheelbarrow" walks on his hands while his teammate steers.

• OVER/UNDER RACE: Partners take turns squatting while the other jumps over, leapfrogging their way to the finish line. Alternatively, they can take turns standing with legs apart while the other crawls through. Or you can combine the two and do both!

• DON'T DROP THE BALL RACE: Partners must pin a ball between their heads or shoulders or hips, then hurry to the finish line without dropping the ball or touching it with their hands.

# -4-
# Relay Races

Relay races are always lots of fun. No baton necessary!
Divide runners into teams, then line up and race to see
which team can complete the following challenges first:

- POTATO RELAY: Each teammate must hold a potato
  between his knees (no hands!) and race around a cone or
  other marker before passing the potato to the next in
  line. Any runner who drops the potato must start over.
  The race is won when all the players on either team
  complete the loop without dropping the potato.

- EGG-TOTING RELAY: Players must run the relay
  while holding a boiled egg on the end of a spoon. If no
  eggs are handy, try using an acorn or a gumball, instead.

- WET-HEAD RELAY: One runner from each team runs
  to a marker and back balancing a cup of water on his
  head, then passes it to the next in line, who follows suit.
  Don't want to get drenched? Use a wet sponge instead.

- COWBOY RELAY: Runners don cowboy hat, boots,
  vest, and bandana, run around the marker, come back to
  the team, and give the clothes to the next in line, who
  wears them for his leg of the race. Continue until all
  have had a turn and one team wins.

6

# -5-
# Distance Running

How about lacing up your running shoes and training for a local charity run as a family? 5K, 10K, the distance doesn't matter.

If you allow the little ones to skate or ride their bikes, they'll have no trouble keeping up with you and the bigger kids while you train. Then on race day, you can all run (or walk) in two groups: tortoises and hares. In our family, Mom usually volunteers to chaperone the former, and Dad does his best to keep up with the latter.

To make it easier to count heads and keep track of kids in the crowd, our family likes to dress in matching shirts on the day of the event. We made turkey handprint shirts for running in our local "Turkey Trot" every Thanksgiving. We painted everybody's palms black and each finger a different color, printed them on the shirts, then added legs, beak, eyes and comb, plus lettering that reads, "Let's Talk Turkey."

We also have black and white spotted T-shirts for the Cowtown Marathon (the same shirts that get us free food from Chick-fil-A on Cow Appreciation Day), and other shirts that say "I'm walking for my brother/son/cousin/life" that we've worn for years at an annual Diabetes Walk.

7

# -6-
# Marathon Mama

Several years ago, my husband convinced me that all my years of childbearing put me in prime cardiovascular condition and that I should, therefore, run a marathon with him the following spring.

Never mind that I hadn't run in years and couldn't even make it between two lampposts without getting winded. All I needed, he assured me, was a little time and determination.

And I was just crazy enough to believe him.

It took a full month for me to work my way up to a mile, but five short months after that, I completed the full 26.2 at his side. I don't know if what we were doing could technically qualify as *running*—it was really more of a 20-mile jog followed by a 6-mile cool down—but I still managed to cross the finish line, hand-in-hand with my husband, before the clock was stopped.

And if I can do it, anyone can.

*"Let us run with endurance the race that is set before us."*
*- Hebrews 12:1*

*Section 2*

# Morning
# Calistenics

# -7-

# Stretch Those Muscles!

Aren't mornings amazing? A fresh new start to a fresh new day! What's not to love about that? Mornings make me want to throw my arms open wide and embrace the coming day with gusto. It feels so good to *strrreeeetch* when you first wake up. Reach high to the sky, fingers out, muscles taut, shoulders back, neck extended, back arched. Hold it…. Hold it….  Hold it….

Then *relax*. Honestly, now. Doesn't that just feel delicious?

Whenever my children seem sluggish (or Mom gets drowsy) during lesson time, we take a little stretch break. We do the same series of stretches I did back in grade school during what my teachers used to call "Morning Calisthenics."

- WINDMILLS: With legs apart and arms extended, bend at waist and touch your toes, alternating right hand to left foot, back up again, then left to right.

- HELICOPTERS: Keeping arms stiff and straight out to your sides, trace tiny circles with your fingertips, then larger circles, first forward, then back. Repeat.

- BUTTERFLIES: Sit on floor with knees out and feet together and bounce knees gently toward the ground.

11

# -8-
# Push Up Competitions

Our kids will do all sorts of calisthenics if we challenge them to a contest with prizes for the winner. We often have push up, sit up, chin up, or handstand competitions in which each and every member of the family will put forth maximum effort, just for a chance to win a free treat from Smoothie King.

It's fun to stage a spur-of-the-moment push-up competition or handstand contest, but we usually try to give the children a little advanced warning, so they can practice up before the big event. Dad or one of their older brothers will make the announcement, "On Friday night, we're going to see who can do the most sit-ups," and the kids are off and running.

Some of them will practice daily, trying to boost their numbers before the big day. Others choose to conserve their energy until it really counts. Either way, a good time is had by all.

We usually divide into age groups, bigs and littles, and award a prize for the top boy and girl in each. Or we'll multiply results by an age-based factor to even things out. That way, the two-year-old and the twelve-year-old can be on more even footing.

# -9-
# Aerobics Videos

Exercise videos can provide another fun and inexpensive way to work out with your children—plus, it's easy to find nearly-new programs for cheap when you buy used.

Several years ago, my husband brought home an extremely intense program called P90-X. This rigorous regimen promised to whip us into shape in just 90 days. Enthusiasm ran high. The master bedroom was transformed into an aerobics class as young and old alike lined up every night before dinner for calisthenics, plyometrics, and kempo karate. We lasted almost two weeks before Mom and Dad ran out of steam and called it quits, beach bodies or no.

I found TTapp videos to be more my speed and lost 30 lbs. of baby fat in three months by doing those twelve minutes of low-impact aerobics every day. Unfortunately, I had trouble getting my children to join me for that routine, as they insisted it was "only for old people." (Not true!)

I've had better luck with them by plugging in some upbeat praise music and letting them make up their own routines and dances. Do whatever works, just as long as you get up and get moving!

# -10-
# Jumping Rope

Forget hand weights, yoga balls, resistance bands, and step platforms. Do you know what was the most popular PE equipment when I was growing up? Jump ropes!

My school had dozens of them in every length imaginable. Short ones for jumping alone. Long ones for jumping while somebody else held the rope. We'd take turns jumping to rhymes like this:

> *Cinderella, dressed in yella,*
> *Went upstairs to kiss a fella,*
> *Made a mistake and kissed a snake,*
> *How many doctors did it take?*
> *1...2...3...4...*

We'd count until we missed, then take a turn holding the rope while the next person jumped. My own children prefer to jump to the rhyme:

> *Ice cream, soda pop, lemonade*
> *Tell me all the letters in your best friend's name.*

Then they start spelling the names of all their siblings. Only a really good jumper can make it to the end of *that* list without missing or stepping on the rope!

14

# -11-
# Jumping Just to Jump

There's nothing quite like jumping to get your heart a-pumping! So let's psyche ourselves out and get ready to spring! There are so many ways to do it:

- JUMPING JACKS: Stand straight with feet together and hands at your side. Keeping your arms straight, jump up and land with feet apart and hands together up over your head. Jump up again and land in starting position. You've just done one Jumping Jack. Give me ten more!

- SQUAT JUMPS: My dad taught me how to do these in junior high. He learned them in the army and thought they might improve my basketball game. They didn't, but they sure toned up my thighs! Clasping your hands behind your head (elbows out) squat on your heels with one knee pointing forward and the other to the side. Leap straight up, landing on your toes and immediately crouching back to starting position, but with knees reversed. Repeat.

- BROAD JUMPS: Our kids love trying to outdo each other's distance on jumping with feet together, feet apart, with or without a running start. Try it at home!

15

# -12-
# Stop, Drop, and Roll

Yes, I know. "Stop, Drop, and Roll" is what you are supposed to do if you ever catch on fire: Running only fans the flames and makes them burn hotter. Rolling on the ground or in the dirt helps to smother the fire and put it out.

But "Stop, Drop, and Roll" is also a great way to get some exercise. You'll need a pair of dice and a list of moves: push ups, sit ups, lunges, squats, jumping jacks, windmills, etc.

The first person in line calls out a move, drops to his knees, and rolls the dice. Whatever number he rolls is the number of reps everybody must do of the move he named.

Once that set has been completed, everyone stops, and the dice are passed to the next person in line, who chooses an exercise, drops to her knees, and rolls to see how many reps the whole group will do that time.

Continue play until all the exercises have been done and/or all the kids have had a turn choosing moves and rolling dice.

# -13-
# Stair Climbing

Whether you're taking one, two, or three steps at a time, climbing stairs makes for a heart-pounding workout.

Although most of the houses our family has lived in have been single-story affairs, our last home had a concealed staircase that led to a schoolroom on the second level. The stairs were well away from the family bedrooms, and I loved being able to climb them in the wee hours of the morning to get in some exercise without disturbing sleepers or leaving home.

Instead of counting flights, I would post a list of people to pray for at the bottom of the staircase, then would pray for a different person each time I climbed up and back down. When I got to the end of my list, I always knew how many flights I'd climbed, because I knew how many people I'd prayed for.

It was a great way to multi-task, and I knew that God could always hear my prayers, even though I was usually too winded to utter them aloud!

*"This is the confidence which we have before Him, that, if we ask anything according to His will, He hears us."*

(1 John 5:14)

17

# -14-
# Sitting on the Wall

My father, whom I adored, was a general contractor, so it makes sense that in eighth grade, I decided to take wood and metal shop as an elective. I learned welding, soldering, and engine repair during the fall semester, then drafting, woodworking, and plastics in the spring.

I was the only girl in the class.

The boys sometimes got a little rowdy, and when they did, my shop instructor had a novel way of settling them down: He'd make them sit on the wall.

To do it, they had to stand with their backs against the wall, then bend their knees and inch their way down until their thighs were parallel to the ground. It looked just like they were sitting in a chair, only there was no chair.

This is much harder than it looks or sounds, as I discovered when I tried it at home (practicing in case I should ever get in trouble in class).

To make it even more challenging, try holding out your arms, as well, straight in front of you and parallel to the ground. How long can *you* hold that position?

*Section 3*

# How to Have a Ball

# -15-
# Kickball

Last summer, our family got on a kickball jag. We played every chance we got and had great fun doing it!

Kickball is played just like baseball as far as outs, fouls, and base running goes. The only difference is that you're rolling and kicking a 9-inch rubber ball instead of pitching and batting a 3-inch leather one.

We did our best to balance our teams so each had roughly the same number of children and adults, boys and girls, athletically gifted players and, for lack of a better descriptor, coordinationally-challenged ones.

Since we had such a wide age range on the field (four years to forty-nine years and everything in between), we also modified the rules to make the game more equitable. Boys over twelve had to kick left-footed, and children under twelve only had to get within ten feet of the base without being tagged for their run to count (we used cones to mark the distance—once they made it past, they were safe).

It worked well, which is why kickball has remained one of our family's favorite sports.

# -16-
# Sandlot Baseball

We have a neighbor whose young son is an amazing baseball pitcher. College scouts are already talking to him, and the boy is only thirteen!

But all that comes at a price. Our friend's family has had to eat, breathe, and sleep baseball for years already, with no end in sight. There's daily practice, special camps, private coaches, weekly (and sometimes twice weekly) games, and out-of-town trips every other weekend with a travel team.

If that is one extreme, our family's approach to baseball is the other: For six Sundays every spring, we meet at a local park with a bunch of other homeschoolers, and the dads coach the kids in a sandlot league. They get twelve hours *total* to practice a few drills, play a few games, hear a few pep talks, eat a few popsicles—then it's over until next year.

How *wonderful* is that?

Will any of our kids get drafted to play college ball? Maybe. Maybe not. Time will tell. But they will enjoy a relaxed and unrushed childhood—as will their parents—free from the domination of a sports association that pushes and pulls families in opposite directions every night of their lives. And that sounds like a reasonable trade-off to me.

# -17-
# Flag Football

Tackle football makes us nervous. We're not interested in all the body contact, head butting, possible concussions, sprains, strains, and broken bones that often accompany the sport. So if you're playing full contact, count us out.

But flag football? That's something else entirely!

Our guys love flag football and play it at family camp every fall and on Sunday afternoons with friends—when they're not playing Frisbee, that is (see Chapter 22).

Instead of tackling the guy with the ball, the opposing team must merely grab a streamer off the belt he's wearing. It's all the fun of regular football with none of the risk.

Well, almost none. We did have a broken collarbone last year. But that was a freak accident.

Normally, sore muscles for the dads (and bruised egos for the boys) are the only casualties that come of these annual father-son matches.

23

# -18-
# Knock-Out

For as long as I can remember, we've had some sort of basketball goal in our driveway. It's handy for playing three-on-three or shooting hoops to burn off energy, but it has also made for some great character training. Learning to win graciously and lose with dignity takes a lot of practice! And playing a quick game of Knock Out each evening after dinner is a perfect way to get it.

To play, you line up in order with two balls. The first in line makes a free throw shot with one ball (then keeps shooting lay-ups until he gets a basket), but as soon as he's taken the first shot, the next in line shoots a free throw followed by lay-ups until she gets one in. If she makes her basket before Player 1 makes his, he gets knocked out of the game. If Player 1 scores first, he passes his ball to the third person in line, who immediately starts trying to knock out Player 2. Last one left in the game wins.

Anyone who fails to control his temper during the game gets to be the "Guest Speaker" at Bible time afterward and read aloud selected passages from *Proverbs for Parenting*, a topical arrangement of Scripture under such headings as anger, pride, patience, and humility. (Sad to say, even Mom and Dad have had to take occasional turns reading choice verses after especially competitive rounds of Knock-Out.)

# -19-
# Tennis

Tennis is truly a life-long sport. All you need is a racquet, a few balls, and a partner (or a backboard), and you're good to go. It's a great way to stay active, far into your golden years and beyond.

Bad habits are hard to break, so we'd recommend taking a couple of lessons upfront to learn proper technique. Many cities offer free lessons for kids during summer months, and community colleges offer inexpensive lessons, as well.

Our children have taken lessons off and on through our local homeschool group. Although our older, more experienced kids enjoy playing singles or doubles, the little guys love to play a game called "Around the World." It's specially designed for big groups, so it is perfect for our family.

Half the group lines up at the baseline on one side of the court and the other half lines up at the opposite baseline. The first person in line hits the ball across the net, then runs around the net to take his place at the back of the line on the other side. Meanwhile, the first person on that side has hit the ball back to the opposite court and run around the net to line up with that side. Any player who fails to return the ball on his turn is out. Play continues until there are only two players left, who then play for points without running to opposite sides of the net each time they hit the ball.

25

# -20-
# Soccer

Soccer can be a fun sport for families, but unless your name is Duggar, you likely don't have enough children to field two complete teams.

Don't let that deter you. Just invite another family to join in or play with fewer than eleven players per team. Back when we had half as many kids as we do now, we played a lot of Cook vs. Flanders games at a park near our house.

Since our family and our friends' families have continued to grow, when we get together now, we have no problem finding enough players.

Sometimes, in fact, we have too many—at least by certain standards, though not by ours! Instead of making someone sit out, we just put an extra ball or two in the game. That makes things *really* interesting.

Our guys were involved in a soccer game just last week that had to be the biggest one yet: Close to a hundred players on the field, with five balls in play and two goalies per team.

It was a blast!

And, best of all, the Flanders' side won. ☺

# -21-
# Ping Pong

My husband is a bit prone to making impulse purchases. Case in point: He once brought home not one, but two top-of-the-line Ping-Pong tables that had been used in a recent World Table Tennis Championship. "The discounted price," said he, "was just too good to pass up."

Our boys love this game. I never knew a person could work up such a sweat playing Ping-Pong until seeing them play!

Word spread about the new tables, and we soon began hosting neighborhood and church tournaments, in addition to our family tournaments. We discovered we had quite a few avid Ping-Pong players in our little circle of friends. Playing table tennis together was a real bonding experience, and we made many lasting memories doing it.

Unfortunately, those tables didn't survive our last move (but we made sure they went to good homes). We still love to play, only now we go to the community center to do it or make do with a clamp-on net on our dining table at home.

Even a scarf strung across the kitchen table with some popsicle sticks and duct tape will do in a pinch—but you've got to really want to play bad to make it work.

27

# -22-
# Ultimate Frisbee

Technically, a Frisbee is a disk, not a ball, but playing Ultimate is an über-fun way to get fit, so I'm including it in this section anyway.

Our family has been playing Ultimate Frisbee for well over a decade now. My husband even bought a bunch of orange and yellow vests so we could play with huge groups of friends and still keep track of who's on whose team.

The games get pretty intense! Although big sisters often join in, I'll admit that most of the moms (myself included) just cheer from the sidelines and work to keep the little ones entertained.

Ultimate Frisbee is played a lot like football, with each team trying to get the disk into the goal at the opposite end of the field. The thing to remember with Frisbee is that one foot must remain fixed for as long as you are in possession of the disk. The key is to *pivot*. Also, beginners should catch two-handed, by sandwiching the disk between their palms.

Once you get really good at playing by day, you may want to invest in an LED lighted disk and some glow-in-the-dark bracelets: Ultimate Frisbee is twice as fun after dark.

Section 4

# Pedal Pushers

# -23-
# Bike Racing

Our boys have biking in their blood: When one of them was three, he hopped on what would soon be his first bicycle—a 16-inch model from Sportstown—pedaled to the front of the store, and parked in front of the cash register. When another was three, he taught himself to ride without training wheels by pushing a brother's bigger bike to the top of a hill to practice pedaling as he coasted back down.

The girls like to ride, too, so we've done lots of biking as a family over the years. Fortunately, we live in a town that has a good network of bike paths and trails, so we can get most places safely on two wheels: We'll bike around the block to wake up in the morning before hitting our books. We'll bike to the neighborhood swimming pool for a dip in the pool during summer months. We'll bike along city park trails, then stop at a little frozen custard shop for a tasty treat before heading home.

Sometimes we'll enter bike races for fun, too. Bigger kids will bike the longer distance (20, 40, sometimes 60 miles). while Mom and the little ones stick to the shorter 1 or 2-mile courses. Either way, biking is a sure recipe for family fun.

31

# -24-
# Slow Down

Have you ever had a S-L-O-W bike race? This is another family favorite and something we do at least once every summer.

We all line up at the start line, then…

*On your mark. Get set. Go!*

…and everyone's off!

Only, in this race, it is the *last* person across the finish line who wins.

It takes a lot of balance. There can be no stopping along the way! Your feet must stay on the pedals and the bike must keep rolling through the entire race. No doubling back, either, or you'll be disqualified.

Sounds simple, doesn't it? Try it and see for yourself: it's not as easy as you think.

And if one of your kids has training wheels, all bets are off!

# -25-
# Bike Rental

Don't live in an area conducive to biking? Or maybe you don't own bikes of your own? Don't let that stop you.

Many tourist towns have rental shops—you might just save biking for when you're on vacation. We've rented surreys for pedaling along the beach in Galveston, cruisers for sightseeing at Hilton Head, and mountain bikes for riding the trails at Yosemite. Check with your hotel to see what's available next time you travel.

Some big cities offer bike sharing, as well. Our kids have used the bike-share program in Austin, and the last time we were in Fort Worth, I noticed a program was available there, too. To find out if bike sharing is available near you, check the world map here: *www.bikesharingworld.com.*

# -26-
# Mountain Biking

Whenever you're ready to take biking to a whole new level, just grab your helmet and head to your nearest State Park for a ride on the nature trails.

Uphill and down, beside lakes, along ledges, over bumpy, gnarled tree roots, under overhangs—trail riding opens up a whole new world.

Be sure to pack extra water and granola bars in your backpack, as mountain biking is hard work, and you may wind up hungry and thirsty a long way from civilization.

To find a mountain bike trail near you, plug in your zip code at *www.singletracks.com* and hit search. They'll display all the known trails in your area and give you a difficulty rating for each of them.

Section 5

Let's
Play Tag

# -27-
# Classic Tag

Classic tag is a simple game of cat and mouse. One person gives chase, and the other players run.

Have you noticed that kids never get too old to enjoy a rousing game of tag? This is especially true when the parents play, too!

Little ones will enjoy just being chased around the front yard, but don't simply tap them when you tag them. Make a big deal of scooping them off their feet, burying your face in their neck, kissing, tickling, and snuggling them until they dissolve into giggles.

Or if your kids are too big to scoop up anymore, try to get their giggles out by playing one of the following variations on the game....

# -28-
# Octopus Tag

When playing Octopus Tag, everybody except one mobile *it* lines up on one side of the yard or field. The end zones on both sides are safety zones, and players cannot be tagged once they are inside that area.

When the mobile *it* yells, "Go!" all the other players must run to the opposite side of the yard, from one safety zone to the other.

As they do, the mobile *it* gives chase, trying to tag as many players as possible. Anyone tagged on the way across becomes a stationary *it*.

The stationary *its* must remain rooted to the spot where they were tagged while trying to help the mobile *it* tag the remaining players on subsequent dashes across the yard.

The field between eventually becomes a maze of stationary *its,* so navigating one's way across without getting tagged takes a great amount of stealth and skill.

The last player tagged gets to be the mobile *it* for the next game.

# -29-
# Freeze Tag

The object of a game of freeze tag is for the person who is *it* to "freeze" everybody at once and make sure they stay frozen. He does this by tagging them and saying, "You're frozen," then running off to tag and freeze all the remaining players.

The person who is *it* must try to do this as quickly as possible, before anybody has a chance to "unfreeze" the players who've been previously frozen, as often happens when some poor frozen soul calls out pleadingly to her teammates, "Unfreeze me! Unfreeze me!"

(Seldom, if ever, does the freezing process extend to the vocal cords.)

And then some merciful and daring teammate will dart in while the *it* isn't watching, and unfreeze the one calling for help by tagging her and saying, "You're unfrozen!"

Yes, I know—technically, it would be just as correct to shout, "You're thawed!" Or to maybe even use the words "melted," "liquefied," or "defrosted."

But that's not how the game is normally played.

# -30-
# Chinese Tag

Chinese tag is just like freeze tag, except when a player gets frozen, he stands with his legs apart. Then to be unfrozen (i.e., thawed), another player must crawl between his legs before the person who is *it* sees and catches them.

This version is much more challenging for the players and much less challenging for the *it,* which makes it a good choice when the one doing the chasing is very much younger than the ones being chased.

Feel free to switch back and forth between freeze tag and Chinese freeze tag as the situation may call for it.

# -31-
# Zombie Tree Tag

To begin a game of Zombie Tree Tag, choose one player to be "the zombie." That person must count to fifteen, then give chase to everyone else.

Anybody the zombie tags will himself become a zombie and must join him in tagging others.

All trees serve as bases, but only for fifteen seconds at a time. Zombies must back 15 feet away from any player on a tree.

Each player gets three trees per game (or the same tree three separate times). Once you're out of trees—and surrounded by zombies—you're out of luck.

The last one tagged is the winner, and the next-to-the-last one tagged serves as the first zombie for the next game.

# -32-
# Swing Tag

For this game, you'll need a fairly narrow swing set (with space for about three swings). Designate a base on either side of the swing set, out of the swings' reach. We use the brick wall of our house on one side and the fence on the other. Toss all but the center swing up out of the way.

One person gets in the remaining swing (it works better if he hooks the swing under his arms and across the belly, rather than sitting in it) and must stay in the swing for the entire game. Everybody else gets on the same base.

When Swing Guy yells *go*, all players must run underneath the swing set and get to the other base without being tagged.

The first person to make it safely to the other base counts to 30. Anybody not on the new base by the time he finishes the count is out. Anybody who gets tagged while running across is also out.

The last untagged person wins and gets to be in the swing for the next game. If the entire group of players makes it from one base to the other three times in a row without anybody being tagged, a new Swing Guy is selected, and the game begins again.

# -33-
# Don't Touch Ground

When I was growing up, I spent quite a bit of my free time playing "Don't Touch Ground." Unfortunately, since my one and only sister was not nearly as tomboyish as I, this normally ended up being a solo performance. I'd climb from our patio onto a wooden fence, then inch around the perimeter of our yard, back to the house and onto our roof, all the while imagining that the grass beneath me was a swamp full of hungry crocodiles who wanted me for lunch.

I must admit, however, that the version my children play is about a hundred times better than that game of my childhood. Being chased by a real person a few steps behind you is ever so much scarier than just pretending to run from imaginary alligators or ferocious tigers or even those flying monkeys out of *The Wizard of Oz*. Especially when those kids combine "Don't Touch Ground" with "Zombie Tag" and you have a whole crowd on your tail!

When we play at the playground, ground means ground. We leap and jump from one piece of equipment to another to avoid being tagged. If we play at home, ground may be concrete (as opposed to grass) or wood floors (as opposed to carpet). Either way, there's always a lot of jumping and climbing involved. And a great deal of fun!

43

## Section 6

# Chalk Up Some Fun

# -34-
# Hop Scotch

Sidewalk chalk makes playing hop scotch so much easier than when I was a girl. Back then, we had to hunt for the right kind of rock that could mark on concrete. Sometimes recess would be almost over before we found one.

With the thick chunks of sidewalk chalk you can now get at any dollar store, you can draw a hopscotch grid quickly, then spend most of your time actually playing the game.

You'll still need a rock, though, for tossing into whichever square you intend to skip over.

To make it into a learning lesson, give kids math problems to do in their heads and have them jump to the square that contains the right answer.

Or put letters instead of numbers in the squares, and have them hop around, spelling simple words. They'll get their exercise *and* a math or spelling review.

47

# -35-
# Road Maps

If your children aren't into hopscotch, try using the sidewalk chalk to draw large, circuitous road maps to use with toy cars—the bigger, the better. Make it cover the entire patio!

You'll get a workout drawing in all the roads and bridges and tracks and parks and walkways. And your kids will get a workout traversing the same with their little four-wheelers.

If you want to add some extra fun to the chalked-in highway system, get a roll of aluminum foil and crimp up the edges (so it will hold water) to make lakes and rivers and streams.

If your little ones don't have any motorboats mixed in with their Matchbox cars, let them make ships out of leaves, twigs, and acorn caps.

# -36-
# Obstacle Courses

You can also use your sidewalk chalk to create simple, two-dimensional obstacle courses for your children. Have them walk along this line, then jump into that circle, then hop in each of these squares then straddle that V...

You get the idea.

Be sure to demonstrate by completing the course yourself before challenging them to do so.

Once they have navigated the first course successfully, let them take a turn drawing a new one. Then *you* can try your skill at that one.

# -37-
# Chalk Portraits

Grab your bucket of sidewalk chalk and head out to the driveway with your family to do some self-portraits. Mom and Dad can help outline all the bodies, then let the kids fill in the details. Be sure to take a picture of the masterpiece once you've finished!

Alternatively, you can just draw the background, then lay down in the middle of it once you're done for a fun photo:

1. Draw clouds and rain, plus a big umbrella for your little one to "hold."

2. Sketch a moon, stars, and a rocket ship, then set her atop of it for a "ride."

3. Draw a city skyline and a superhero cape, then pose your child like he's flying over the city.

4. Draw a rainbow and a balloon with a basket and a dog, then let your daughter float to Oz like Dorothy.

You'll need to use a ladder to get the best camera angles. Trust me, Mom and Dad—you'll get plenty of exercise climbing up and down to snap pictures!

# -38-
# Four-Square

Our guys learned how to play four-square at a father-son retreat about fifteen years ago. They came straight home and taught the rest of us how to play—without even pausing long enough to unpack—and we've been hooked ever since.

To play, use your sidewalk chalk to draw a large square and divide it into four sections. Number the squares 1-4, grab a ball (a rubber kickball works nicely), and you're ready to play.

| 1 | 2 |
|---|---|
| 4 | 3 |

Station one player in each square, with additional players lined up outside the square, waiting their turn. The player in Square 4 begins each round by serving the ball to the player in Square 2. That player lets it bounce (once and only once) before hitting it into the square of another player. If it bounces twice, or the player is unable to return it, or he hits it out of the court, the receiving player is out and must go to the end of the line of players waiting for their turn to play.

Meanwhile, all the remaining players move up a square, and the first in line takes his place in Square 1. The object of the game is to eliminate the players in the squares above yours so that you can move to the highest square yourself, then stay there as long as possible.

51

*Section 7*

Keep Your Balance

# -39-
# Tight-Rope Walking

Every Christmas, our children get a stocking full of goodies from Mom and Dad, a gift from their "Secret Santa" (the kids draw names to determine who buys for whom), and a family gift we all share.

Two years ago, the family gift was a slack-line, which we installed between two trees in our backyard. It's a little like a tightrope, only flatter, closer to the ground, and not as taut.

It took several weeks of trying before anyone made it across without falling. One child would get up as early as 4 AM to get in extra practice time without having to wait in line. She now holds the family record for consecutive crosses—33½ times without falling.

Slack lining is a fun way to improve balance, but it's not the only way. For very young children, just drawing a chalk line or taping a length of rope to the floor provides a good challenge. Once they've mastered that, let them walk along curbs, on landscaping timbers, or across a 2x4 laid on the ground. When they're ready to test their skill on a slack line, Google it to see what's available or visit Timberdoodle.com, which is where I got ours.

# -40-
# Pogo Sticks

We bought our pogo stick at a garage sale for a couple dollars several years ago. I brought it home, and the whole family immediately set about trying to master it.

Our son Samuel (ten years old at the time) outshined us all, though, and without much practice. His record? 1100 consecutive bounces.

He set it while waiting for the rest of the family to get loaded into the van—and only stopped then so he wouldn't make us late to wherever we were going.

He even took the pogo stick to Family Camp that year and strutted his stuff in the annual talent show: two handed, one handed, no handed, grinning ear to ear the whole time.

I think we made him stop before he fell off that time, too.

A few siblings tried to top his record, but none came very close. Impressed with Samuel's skill, we Googled the World Pogo Stick Record, suspecting he *must* be pretty close. Ha!

So if you get your kids a pogo stick, they may be able to break the Flanders family record. But be forewarned: If they want to break the Guinness World Record, they'll have to bounce 206,865 times in a single stretch to do so!

# -41-
# Handstand Contests

Do you want to know a fast, cheap, and easy way to improve your balance and strengthen core muscles? Practice doing handstands!

If your children are new to standing on their hands, they may want to practice against the wall or the back of a sofa until they start to get the feel for it and develop some strength in their arms.

Once they get to a point that they can stay balanced without support (or without flailing about) for at least a full minute, they may be ready for some of these challenges.

1. SCISSOR MOVE: Keeping legs perfectly straight, split them apart, and then bring them back together without losing your balance. Repeat.

2. ONE-HANDED: Balance on one arm. Once you get that move down, try switching to the other arm and back without falling.

3. VERTICAL PUSH UPS: Slightly arch your back and bend at the elbows while slowly lowering your face toward the floor, then straighten your arms again and return to starting position.

57

# -42-
# King of the Mountain

This is a game we play almost every time we eat out, provided the parking lot isn't too crowded. Once we've finished our dinner and are walking back to our car, we'll find an isolated curb (those rounded parking guides that keep cars from pulling too far into a space) and see who can remain "King of the Mountain" the longest.

We normally play littlest to biggest, so the two youngest members of the family go first and the rest of us line up to watch and wait our turns. The players balance themselves upon the curb, one at either end, facing one another.

As soon as the younger one calls, "Ready. Set. Go." they inch forward and join right hands. Each player then uses his weight to try to push or pull the other off balance without losing balance himself.

The first person to step off the curb loses and goes to the back of the line. The victor remains on the curb to face the next challenger.

We sometimes play several rounds, but whoever's still on the curb when it's time to go home gets to keep the title "King of the Mountain"—at least, until next time. ☺

# -43-
# Juggling

Do you think juggling is just for magicians, clowns, and circus performers? Think again.

Juggling is a great way to improve balance and hand-eye coordination, so give it a try. It's much easier, though, if you begin by juggling scarves instead of balls. They stay in the air longer and don't roll away if they hit the ground.

Beginning with two scarves in your left hand and one in your right, toss one of the scarves from the left hand into the air and catch it with the right. Just before you do, though, release the scarf that is in your right hand, and catch it with the left, after releasing the remaining scarf from the left.

Continue in this fashion as long as you can. After the initial toss, you should never have more than one scarf at a time in either hand. When working with scarves, it's almost as if you are *pulling* (rather than throwing) them up into the air, but it will help you get the timing and motion of juggling down, so that you will hopefully have better success when you switch to balls.

It takes a little practice, but once you get the hang of it, you'll never forget.

# Section 8

## Heart-Healthy Housekeeping

# -44-
# Ten-Minute Room Rescue

Raising a family of any size is a lot of work, but then again, "many hands make light labor." The chores can be quite enjoyable when done together with happy hearts.

Younger children are especially eager to work, and they take pride in helping. If you cultivate this attitude in your little ones, you will still have cheerful workers when they grow older.

Start small, by having toddlers pick up their own toys and put them away when they are finished playing. Of course, when lots of different children get together and play with lots of different toys, this can look like a more daunting task than it actually is.

Try setting a timer and conducting a "ten-minute room rescue." Have everybody pick up and put away ten or fifteen or twenty items, depending on how cluttered the area has become. If everybody works together for ten minutes, I guarantee the place will look better when the timer goes off.

As your children get used to working this way, they probably won't need the full ten minutes. My kids can usually rescue a room in five.

# -45-
# Don't Stop the Music

Want to get the housework done in a hurry? Plug in some lively, upbeat music, and then try to finish small pieces of the job before the next song is over.

We own a collection of 50's music—bought years ago at a gas station in the middle of a desert while my husband was stationed in El Paso—that is perfect for this purpose. The first song on the CD is "Yakkity-Yak." I can't think of a more fun or appropriate song for housecleaning:

*Take out the papers and the trash*
*Or you don't get no spendin' cash*
*If you don't scrub that kitchen floor*
*You ain't gonna rock and roll no more*
*Yakety yak (Don't talk back)*

*Just finish cleanin' up your room*
*Let's see that dust fly with that broom*
*Get all that garbage out of sight*
*Or you don't go out Friday night*
*Yakety yak (Don't talk back)* *

It's also a great song to dance to, which is what we usually end up doing once the work is done!

* Songwriters: Jerry Leiber & Mike Stoller © Sony/ATV Music Publishing LLC

# -46-
# Cleaning by Color

This cleaning game may take a little longer than normal, but it's a good way to motivate hesitant helpers when they are little and overwhelmed with the number of blocks on the floor that must go in the bucket.

Call out a color—"Blue!"—then work alongside your little one to find all the blue blocks and put them away.

Once the blues are returned to their proper home, pick another color—"Red!" —and keep on working.

Repeat until the job is completed and the room looks tidy.

By the way, the game works for other things beside blocks, too. And it's a good one to play while Mom is nursing the baby or sick on the couch. She can give directions and let the children scurry about the room, hunting appropriately colored items to return to their rightful homes.

# -47-

# Room to Room

One way to do chores is to make assignments and work independently: One child cleans the bathrooms and another cleans the kitchen while you do laundry.

This method can work, but if your children have a hard time staying on task, you'll probably get the house clean faster by all staying together and tackling a room at a time.

In the kitchen, for instance, one child can unload the dishwasher, another wash off counters, another sweep the floors, and another wipe down the fronts of the appliances while you scour the stovetop. The work gets done in short order when everybody pitches in.

Give the littlest ones less critical, pint-size chores:

- Dusting mini-blinds with feather duster
- Cleaning fingerprints off cabinets and door-knobs with spray bottle full of water or a child-safe cleaner
- Cleaning scuff marks off linoleum with baking soda or toothpaste
- Washing dust off baseboards with a damp cloth

Once the kitchen is clean, move to the living room and make new assignments: one child vacuums, one dusts, one cleans out from under the sofa cushions, etc.

# -48-
# Let's See the Dust Fly with that Broom

One of my favorite scenes in the movie *The Village* is when the young girls are dancing and spinning in circles while sweeping their front porch. Tevye's daughters did the same thing in *Fiddler on the Roof.*

Who ever said sweeping had to be a drudgery? Sweeping is great exercise for your arms, shoulders, abdominals, and oblique. Plus, if you sing or dance or whistle while you work, it can be quite enjoyable.

I remember when our oldest daughter was eight, we once left her indoors to sweep up after dinner while the rest of us went outside to finish some yard work before dark. A new neighbor stopped by to chat with us as we were bagging leaves and ended up watching our daughter through the front window the whole time we visited. Bethany was in there, cheerfully singing and sweeping away, totally oblivious that anybody could see her. The neighbor was impressed with this daughter's happy attitude, and said so repeatedly. Which is why we should always *"do [our] work heartily, as for the Lord rather than men."* (Colossians 3:23) Because you never know who might be watching.

67

# Section 9

## Great Chores Outdoors

# -49-
# Garden Growing

Whether you're raising flowers or vegetables, give your kids a patch to call their own. Let them prepare it, plant it, weed it, and reap it.

Letting children get their hands dirty is the best way I know to raise a new crop of avid gardeners.

If gardening flowers, let them pick bouquets. Daisies, black-eyed Susans, chrysanthemums and hydrangeas are all easy to grow and make beautiful, long-lasting bouquets.

Teach them how to divide bulbs and grow plants from cuttings, as well. Lilies, hostas, and lariope are prime candidates for multiplying this way.

If growing food, choose things your children would like to eat. Tomatoes, cucumbers, carrots, and onions are good choices for beginners. Vegetable gardening can turn even the pickiest eater into a salad lover when he grows what he eats in his own backyard.

# -50-
# Lawn Mowing

A friend of mine once confided to me that her favorite household chore is mowing the lawn. I assumed she just enjoyed being out in the fresh air and sunshine, but no, she explained, "I like to cut the grass because once I'm done, I know I won't need to mow again for a week!"

Not so with any other domestic task.

I can see her point and will admit that I like the sense of accomplishment I feel when I mow the grass, too.

Whether my sons like this feeling as well, or they just like earning some extra spending money (lawn mowing is one of the few chores we pay our kids to do), I never have trouble finding a volunteer for the job.

By the time our boys are 10-12 years old, they are big and strong enough to handle a lawnmower without trouble. The younger ones sometimes beg for the job, but we normally make them wait until they're a bit older.

Three things make this work: First, we don't have a power-driven lawnmower. Those tend to run away from you if you aren't careful. Second, the boys wear closed-toe shoes to work. And third, an older person does the weed whacking.

72

# -51-
# Car Washing

Down here in Texas, cars can get really dirty really fast, what with all the red dirt and bugs splattered across our windshields.

But Dad likes them to look clean, and that means a lot of washing. He'll usually take them to a drive-thru carwash down the street, unless our boys are hankering to earn some money, in which case he'll give the job to them.

A big pail of sudsy water, a couple of bulky sponges, and a water hose, and they're all set. And, as any *Karate Kid* fan well knows, that repetitive wax on, wax off motion makes for a marvelous workout!

Texas summers aren't just dirty; they're dangerously hot, so we leave our cars locked in the driveway to make sure little ones don't crawl inside and get cooked. If the car washers want to detail the insides, too, they must wait for the cool of the evening and get the keys from Dad to do so.

# -52-
# Dog Walking

Walking the dog is a calm and relaxing way to get in a little exercise… but what if the only pets you own are three red-eared sliders and an unusually friendly goldfish?

Sloshing around the block with a fishbowl in a wagon isn't quite the same as being hurried along by a leashed ball of fur, is it?

It's been about ten years since our family has owned a dog, but our son Joseph didn't let that fact discourage him. He simply volunteered to walk our neighbors' dogs, instead.

Before we knew it, he was walking six or seven miles a day and getting paid great money to do it. He'd walk one of them at 7:00 sharp every morning, and another each evening after he'd finished all his lessons.

He even printed up business cards to advertise his services and eventually expanded it into pet sitting, as well. And since he'd usually stop by home on his final loop around the block, his siblings got to pet the puppies, too. It gave the rest of us all the benefits of dog ownership, but with none of the responsibility. A real win-win.

# -53-
# Clean-Up Crew

Whenever a particularly heavy storm passes through our neck of the woods, it tends to knock a lot of twigs, sticks, and branches out of our trees. Sometimes the yard is completely littered with them when we wake up the next morning.

Several years ago, Doug hit on a method for tidying up the yard fast: He calls the whole family to come help and has us stand shoulder to shoulder on one side of the yard. Each of us then walks forward in a straight line, picking up all the debris in our path. Just a couple of sweeps in the front yard and a couple more in the back, and we're finished in short order.

Now that we have five grandsons who love to come see us, Grandpa assigns them the job of clearing all the pinecones and sweet gum balls out of our yard. He puts a nominal bounty on each cone they collect, our younger kids pitch in to help, as well, and they all hunt until every last cone is collected.

The children love getting to earn some spending money, Doug loves having a pristine yard, and I love the break, as this "job" keeps all our little ones outside picking stuff up instead of inside dragging stuff out. ☺

# Section 10

Let's Get
Wet & Wild

# -54-
# Visit a Splash Pad

Does your city have a water park?

I don't mean one of those huge amusement parks that cost a small fortune in admission.

I mean a place where kids can play in a fountain. A sprayground. A splash pad.

Our city built one of these a few years back, and it's one of the most popular hangouts in town for the ten-and-under crowd. Families congregate there in the hot summer months to picnic and play.

Children can run under waterfalls, splash through puddles, spray one another with mounted water cannons, or just stand under buckets, waiting for them to tip.

The park is free and open to the community. To find a splash pad near you, Google the name of your town plus the word "sprayground."

Have fun, and stay cool!

# -55-
# A Brave Way to Shave

Want to get Dad in on the fun? Coat his face with shaving cream, then let the kids take turns trying to squirt it off from a distance using the water pistols they bought from the dollar store.

This activity makes a great party game, too. Invite a few other families to join you, then line up all the Dads, coat their faces with shaving cream, and award a prize to the team of children who shoot it clean the fastest.

Don't forget to take pictures, or—better yet—a video! Mom and sisters will want to see this at home!

# -56-
# Water Sprinkler Fun

For some good, old-fashioned fun in your own backyard, turn on the water sprinkler on a hot, dry day and cool off with your kids in its refreshing spray.

- Run through the rainbow mist.

- Turn cartwheels in the grass.

- Hook a hose over your swing set's slide for a homemade water slide.

- Screw an attachment nozzle on the hose and shower one another with the shooting stream.

Once you finish, shut off the spigot and wind up the hose. The lawn got watered and the kids were entertained. That's a two-for-one bonus!

# -57-
# Slip and Slide

Remember those long plastic "Slip & Slides" you could hook up to your water hose to cool off in the summertime? Weren't those things lots of fun?

I don't know whether stores sell them anymore, but you can achieve the same effect with a plastic painter's tarp or two. Just attach them end-to-end with a little duct tape to make your slide as long as you want it.

Put it at the top of a hill and add a little water, then cruise your way down to the bottom.

Don't try to surf across the thing—you might fall and hit your head. Instead, just flop down face first and fly downhill on your belly.

Then make your way back to the top of the hill and cruise down again. Repeat.

# -58-
# Blow Soap Bubbles

Who can resist the simple charm of a beautiful bevy of soap bubbles floating on a summer breeze?

You can mix the solution up yourself using the following recipe:

> *1/2 cup dishwashing soap*
> *5 cups water*
> *2 tbsp. of glycerin (find it at your local drugstore)*

Just use this solution to refill the smaller bubble containers and re-use those little plastic wands for blowing your bubbles.

If those aren't available, pour the mixture into a shallow pan and use cookie cutters, recycled rings from six-pack sodas, or larger loops made from wire clothes hangers as bubble blowers.

# -59-
# Water Gun Fights

As a mother, I totally don't understand the popularity of water guns among my sons, but they love them. Especially the super-soaker variety, with the massive water tanks mounted over the barrel. Ever seen one of those?

But water makes for an easier clean up than paintball or airsoft, so we establish a few ground rules...

- No shooting at somebody's face
- No shooting in the house
- No reloading in the house
- No shooting after someone says *STOP*

... and let them have their fun.

Sometimes, they divide into teams and stage a water war. Sometimes they set up little targets and practice their aim. Sometimes Mom watches from the safety of the house... and sometimes I join in the game!

Look out! Here I come!

# -60-
# Balloon Toss

Our family has a love/hate relationship with balloons. The kids love them. Dad hates them.

More specifically, Dad hates the potential choking threat that balloons pose to babies. So we seldom ever play with balloons at home, and we certainly don't stage many water balloon wars at our house, although some of our kids seem convinced doing so would be the best summer fun possible.

Twice a year, however (once on Memorial Day, then again on the Fourth of July), Dad allows the kids to participate in a water balloon toss at our local swimming pool.

Partners line up a foot away from one another for the first toss. If the balloon drops to the ground or bursts upon being caught, that team's out. Otherwise, the catchers all take one giant step backward and toss the water balloon back to their teammate.

The bigger the space between players grows, the faster those balloons begin to burst. The last team left with an intact water balloon wins.

Just be sure to pick up all the broken fragments of rubber once the game is over. (Or play with raw eggs, instead.)

# -61-
# The Bucket Brigade

To play this game, divide into two teams. It works best to have at least three players per team, but the more, the merrier!

Each team must line up between a bucket full of water and an empty pitcher (both equivalent in size and shape to the bucket and pitcher being used by the opposing team). Additionally, each player will need a small disposable cup.

At the count of three, the first player in each line uses his cup to scoop water out of his bucket and transfer it to the cup of the next person in line. The second person then pours the water into the cup of the third, and so on down the line, until the last player pours (whatever is left of) the water into the pitcher.

Meanwhile, the first player continues to scoop and pour and scoop and pour water, to keep it coming down the line. To make the game more of a challenge, require players to only pass the water over their shoulders and behind their backs.

The first team to fill their (formerly) empty pitcher to the brim wins.

# Section 11

Back to Nature

# -62-
# Of Robins & Salt Shakers

When I was a young girl, my grandfather told me an amazing secret. He said if I could get close enough to a sparrow to sprinkle salt on its tail, I could catch it. I asked if that trick worked for robins, too, and he assured me it did.

Well, Mema and Papa's yard was always chock full of these feathered friends, and I spent many a long morning out on their lawn, salt shaker in hand, running to and fro, trying to pelt those poor birds on their tails.

I never did catch one, though I am certain they couldn't all have escaped unsalted.

It wasn't until I was much older that I came to understand my grandfather's point. It wasn't the salt, but the proximity that was key in that condition. What he told me was true: If I were close enough to sprinkle salt on a sparrow's tail, I'd be close enough to just reach out and grab it.

I also came to realize (eventually) that hurling handfuls of salt from four feet away does not a sprinkle constitute.

# -63-
# Start a Collection

Rocks. Leaves. Bugs. Shells. Fossils. Seeds. So many things in nature lend themselves to collecting.

Encourage your children to collect samples of something that interests them.

Keep your eyes peeled for new specimens wherever you go. Be on the watch while hiking or gardening or beach combing together.

Teach your children how to sort and classify and organize their collection(s).

Get excited about the things that excite them, and help them add to their collection whenever you can.

# -64-
# Take a Hike

Did you know studies have shown spending time with nature reduces stress and promotes longer attention spans? That's a good thing—one that would benefit children and parents alike.

Why not put that knowledge to use by taking a long hike with your kids? If you need help finding a park or nature trail near you, try searching by zip code on this website: *http://www.nwf.org/NatureFind.aspx*

Be sure to pack some water, a few granola bars, and maybe even a first aid kit, especially if you'll be traveling very far from home.

If your children aren't too young, you might even try going on a night hike. Go when the moon is full and bright, and bring along your flashlights to look for nocturnal animals, insects, and plants. Tread as quietly as possible, so you won't frighten them off.

# -65-
# Scavenger Hunt

To make hiking more fun for your little ones, try turning it into a scavenger hunt. If you visit our family website (*www.flandersfamily.info*), you can download free copies of the printable pictured here to use for this purpose.

**SCAVENGER HUNT**

| | | | |
|---|---|---|---|
| blade of grass | lobed leaf | sweet gum ball | smooth rock |
| a wild flower | acorn | compound leaf | doodle bug |
| a snail shell | pine needles | pine cone | handful of sand |
| rough rock | a wild berry | stick or twig | elliptical leaf |
| palmate leaf | dandelion | seed pod | some moss |

Print enough of them that each person in your family can have one, and then carry them with you when you go.

Bring along a pen, as well, to mark off items as you spot them. First one to fill an entire row wins.

Have fun, and happy hunting!

# -66-
# Go Berry Picking

Blackberries grow wild where we live in East Texas. You can find them every April in fields and creek beds (watch for snakes!), and along roadsides and greenbelts.

When we see them start to ripen, we take our buckets and berry baskets, hike through the woods to the nearest patch, and pick them by the pint.

One of our children was born during blackberry season, so many a year we've celebrated his birthday by lighting candles on a cobbler instead of a cake.

If you don't live close to a wild thicket, check to see if there's a pick-your-own farm in your neck of the woods. That's where we go for blueberries during the summer.

You'll want to pick them in the cool of the morning—it isn't as much fun with the sun beating down on your backs—and bring plenty of water.

Freeze anything you can't eat right away, then use them in pies, pancakes, popsicles, and smoothies all year long.

Mmm-mmm-mmmm. They're lip-smacking good!

# -67-
# Tree Climbing 101

The rule at our house is, if you're big enough to get up in a tree by yourself, you're big enough to climb it.

But no propping toddlers on the lowest limb for a head start! They've got to climb up by themselves or wait until they're older and abler.

Obviously, some trees are more conducive to climbing than others. What child (or adult) can resist exploring a sprawling oak whose limbs spread horizontally across the ground?

A sturdy crepe myrtle makes a nice tree for little ones to climb—multiple trunks with smooth limbs for grasping.

Pines present more of a challenge, but a couple of our little monkeys can scale those things in seconds flat!

I, myself, spent a lot of time in a non-bearing mulberry as a child. I'd roost up there for hours, reading books, eating snacks, and trying to coax my Chihuahua into staying in a basket long enough for me to haul her up, too. (She refused.)

If your child is a climber, just make sure she knows to only climb on the green limbs, to never put her weight on a branch that isn't as thick as her wrist, and to test her footing before letting go of one handhold to grab another.

# -68-
# Lake Front Fun

There are so many fun, fitness-promoting things a family can do at the lake! Whether you camp out or just go for the day, visit as often as you have an opportunity to do so.

While you are there, take a long hike through the woods (see Chapter 65), then work your way down to the waterfront.

If equipment is available to do so, take a canoe or kayaking trip together, or hold a family paddleboat race.

Gather some smooth, flat stones and teach your children how to skip them off the water surface. Compete to see who can skip theirs the farthest.

Dig your own worms and go fishing (make sure you have a license to do so if you are at a state or public park). There's not a lot of physical activity involved here, but what's a trip to the lake without a little fishing?

If you stay until dark, be sure to build a campfire and roast marshmallows. Listen to the crickets chirping and the frogs croaking and enjoy the evening together.

# -69-
# Butterflies
# & Lightning Bugs

As much as I love the idyllic images of pretty young girls in their old-fashioned dresses flittering about the garden with butterfly nets in hand, we try to encourage our own children to enjoy these marvelous creatures without touching or attempting to catch them. Their fragile wings are just too easily damaged.

I don't have any qualms about (carefully) catching lightning bugs, however. Remember those?

We used to call them fireflies, and I can remember chasing them in the moonlight on our summer evenings at the lake. My father would poke a few holes in the lid of a jar, and I'd use it to collect a dozen or so of these fascinating insects before he told me to turn them loose, because it was time to go home.

It always makes me happy to see lightning bugs blinking on and off in the distance, as it sets those sweet memories of childhood floating back through my mind.

# -70-
# Horseback Riding

Unless you live on a ranch or in the countryside, horseback riding may be one of those things that gets relegated to your list of vacation-only activities.

Nevertheless, do try to take your children for a short trail ride if you get the chance.

And if you don't? Well, I've yet to meet a toddler who would pass up a "horsey ride" on Dad's back or Grandpa's knee, so offer plenty of those while your children are still young enough to enjoy them.

To make it even more memorable, be sure to sing "Yankee Doodle" while you're bucking about, or chant the rhyme my Daddy always chanted for me:

> *Ride a little horsey*
> *Into town!*
> *Oops, little horsey,*
> *Don't fall down!*

Make a big deal on that last line of nearly dropping them to the ground. The giggles this generates are priceless!

# Section 12

## Getting Fit Out & About

# -71-
# Parks & Playgrounds

Next time you take your children to a playground, remember: There's no rule that says parents are only allowed to sit and watch.

So get up and get moving. If you look for them, you'll find lots of ways to join in the fun and get a good workout at the same time:

- Use the park bench for stretching or doing lunges

- Do side hops over the balance beam

- Try a step routine on a low retaining wall

- Use monkey bars for chin ups or hanging crunches

- Do scissor kicks while you're swinging

- Seesawing makes for great modified squat jumps

- Play tag with your kids, or "Don't Touch Ground"

Your children will love having you join them at play, and you'll love how you feel after this family-friendly workout!

# -72-
# A Trip to the Zoo

Pack the camera and some bottled water and take a walk on the wild side at your local zoo.

Skip the monorail, sightseeing bus, or miniature train—at least for the first hour or two of your visit. Hiking from enclosure to enclosure will give your family a good workout, and you can rest and ride later in the day, once you've gotten in a good walk.

Be sure to bring a little cash to buy animal food for the petting zoo (and snow cones for the children).

If your kids really love the zoo and there's a good one close to home, consider investing in a family membership. It will get you back in for a full year (with no additional charge) and usually offers reciprocal benefits to zoos and animal parks all across the nation.

That way, you can keep walking on the wild side, wherever you may roam.

# -73-
# Roller Skating

Do you remember *roller skates*?

I'm not talking about those new inline styles with their slick, narrow wheels lined up in a single row along the bottom. I mean those old, clunky, beige boots with the mile long laces and chunky rubber wheels riveted in pairs to the four corners of the foot. Remember those?

Believe it or not, roller skates are still around. One church in town has a whole room filled with rack upon rack of those things. They allow our homeschool to group check them out every Friday afternoon and skate around the gym for a couple of hours, for *free*. There's no strobe lights or disco music, but the rest of the nostalgia is still there, and our kids have a blast!

Take your children skating, if you can. Loop the rink hand-in-hand with each child at least once for a "Couples Skate." Stage a few speed skating races. Show them how to play "Crack the Whip."

And don't forget to do the "Hokey Pokey" before you go, because, as we all know... *that's what it's all about*.

# -74-
# Bowling for Dollars

There was a show on TV when I was growing up called *Bowling for Dollars*. It was not the kind of program that would keep a child riveted for long, but I remember my Dad sometimes watching it.

He and my mother bowled together in the days before my sister and I came along. They even had their own shoes and monogrammed bowling balls, which I sometimes borrowed whenever our church youth group held an all night bowling/ skating/ Putt-Putt party, along with all the other Baptist youth groups in town. (If only I could have reversed my bowling and golf scores, I would have done pretty well.)

My parents' shoes and balls are long gone now, but we still take our kids to the bowling ally on occasion. Fortunately, they are all better bowlers than I am. Some of them are very serious about the game and try to improve their form on every turn. Others try to outdo one another with their silly approaches, hopping, skipping, spinning, or even walking on their hands to set their ball loose in the lane.

We don't offer a cash prize like that old TV game show did, but we do usually promise a candy bar to the person with the highest score. And a good time is had by all….

# -75-
# Putt-Putt Golf

We don't go golfing very often—individually or as a family—but there are some pretty elaborate Putt-Putt courses across the country, so we occasionally find time for a game when we are traveling. A trip to Hot Springs in Arkansas would especially not feel complete without putting around at Pirate's Cove.

When playing with a large family, we have found it best to let the little ones go first.

Sure, it may take them half a dozen strokes or more to get the ball in the hole, but once they move ahead, you'll be able to keep your eye on them while taking your time with the more serious players.

We like to keep score. Dad usually awards prizes at the end of the game: one to the player with the best score and another to the player with the most holes-in-one.

The most popular prize? An extra-large snow cone from the vendor on Central Avenue. (The remaining players just get a small.)

# Pool Party Games

# -76-
# Family Diving Exhibition

Our guys love trying to outdo one another on the diving board every summer. They really know how to put on a good show! The girls jump, too, but aren't nearly as daring as Dad and the boys—although a couple of summers ago, I did learn to do a fairly decent backflip, thanks to expert coaching from Doug. Here are our family's favorite moves:

- cannonball (knees to chest and make a big splash!)
- dive (sometimes in jack-knife form)
- front flip
- back flip
- forward 1½ (a front flip that ends in a dive)
- full 360 (a dive with a twist)
- gainer (jump forward, but flip backward)
- reverse gainer (jump backward, but flip forward)
- double front (two full rotations before hitting the water, feet first)

Be sure to video your kids' tricks off the diving board at least once a summer. They'll enjoy critiquing their moves at home—seeing themselves in action can help them improve their performance. To take it up a notch, float an inflatable swim ring below the board and see how many of the above moves you can do before landing in the center hole.

# -77-

# Hunting for Sunken Treasure

When your children are little, you'll want to play this game in the shallow end of the pool.

Toss a few coins in the water, then encourage your kids to hunt until they find them.

This is a sneaky way to get reluctant swimmers to put their face in the water, but it works!

Older children will enjoy playing this game in the five-foot end—especially if they get to keep the coins they find.

If you want to dive for treasure in water deeper than six feet, use diving rings or sticks instead of loose change.

They'll be easier to spot and grasp off the bottom.

# -78-
# Water Volleyball

String a net across the pool and gather your family for a fun round of water volleyball. It's best to have at least two or three players on each side, and use an inflatable beach ball to play (the bigger the better).

The rules differ slightly from normal volleyball: The game is played to 25 (must win by 2) points, the ball must be returned over the net within three hits, the same player may not hit it twice in succession, and once the serving team loses a point, the serve goes to the other side.

Unfortunately, the volleyball net at our community pool somehow got shredded this summer before we got a chance to play, but Doug and I and our six-year-old Gabriel did team up last week against some talented young teens for a three-on-three game of water basketball.

*They* won (but just barely).

# -79-
# Sharks & Minnows

Our children love playing "Sharks and Minnows" at the pool. It's especially fun when we're staying in a hotel, as those pools are normally small and seldom crowded.

To play, one person is selected to be a shark, and everybody else is a minnow. The shark gets out of the pool and stands at the edge with his back to the pool and his eyes closed, halfway between one end of the pool and the other.

Down in the water, the minnows line up on one wall and prepare to swim to the opposite wall when the shark says, "Go!" (Although they are not required to leave the wall immediately).

The shark waits until he thinks the minnows are getting close enough to catch, then turns around and jumps into the water. If, however, he turns around before any minnows have even left the wall, he must stay on dry ground, take one giant step away from the pool, and start over again.

Any minnows he catches are out. Unless you want to make it really challenging for the remaining players, in which case those caught become sharks, too, and must get out of the pool to give chase with the original shark in all subsequent rounds. The last uncaught minnow wins the game.

# -80-
# Marco Polo

To play Marco Polo, the player who is it (whom I'll call Marco) chases all the other players in the pool, but he must keep his eyes closed to do it. Since he cannot see, he must guess at the other players' positions by following their voices.

To facilitate this, every time Marco shouts "Marco," everyone else must call, "Polo" (unless they are under water at the very instant he says it).

Players continue to answer "Polo" whenever they hear "Marco," and Marco keeps following the sound of their voices (no peeking!) until he tags one of them.

The first one tagged becomes the new Marco, and the game continues in like fashion.

# -81-
# Water Aerobics

During the summer after my sixth child was born, I took a water aerobics class to help lose my baby fat. I toted my little one along with me to class, where he was known as "the Michelin Tire Baby," in reference to the inner tube in which he floated during class.

The following summer, I got my workout chasing that same baby, now a toddler, around the perimeter of the pool. No longer content to sit in an inflatable pool toy, he was much more interested in trying on all the flip-flops and aqua shoes he found poolside than in getting in the water. And the closer I was behind him, trying to keep him out of other swimmers' stuff, the faster he'd trot to get ahead of me. Many a lifeguard had to blow their whistle at Little Joe, reminding him to "Walk, don't run!"

Flash forward sixteen years, and Joseph's not so little anymore. Six-foot four with strong muscles and a deep tan, he's sitting on the lifeguard stand himself this summer, blowing his whistle at any swimmers who try to run when they're supposed to walk (including my own grandbabies, who do their best to keep their mama hopping—especially at the pool!)

*Section 14*

Rainy Day Fun

.

# -82-
# Play Charades

Person? Place? Thing? Idea? Book? Movie? Song? You've got to act it out while your team tries to guess. But remember, you can only use hand and body motions to lead your teammates to the right answer. No talking (or fingerspelling) allowed!

Children of all ages love a rousing game of charades. Even those who are normally shy will want to act something out once the game gets going. Play with just your family until everyone gets a little experience and feels comfortable with how the game is played, then try playing with a bigger group: Kids against adults. Boys against girls. One family against another. Mix it up a bit.

Stumped for ideas? Try visiting this charades website. It will let you pick the category, then generate ideas faster than you can act them out: *www.charades-ideas.com*.

# -83-
# Musical Chairs

Almost as iconic a party game as Pin-the-Tail-on-the-Donkey, Musical Chairs has been around for a long, long time. I remember playing it, not only at my own birthday parties, but at the parties of all my little preschool friends.

But—*newsflash!*—playing this game is actually more fun with teens than it is with toddlers. Far more laughter, and far fewer tears when one of them finds himself without a chair.

If you somehow missed this game growing up or have forgotten how it is played, here is a little refresher:

You will need one fewer chairs than the number of people playing the game. Place those chairs in a tight circle with the seats facing outward. As long as the music is playing, the people walk in a circle around the group of chairs, but when the music stops (in the middle of the song, please—don't wait for the end), everyone scrambles to find a seat as quickly as possible to avoid being stuck without a chair. The person left standing is out.

Remove a chair from the circle and begin again with the remaining players. Repeat until there is only one player left, who is then declared the winner.

# -84-
# Can't Catch Me
# Before I Get Upstairs

This is just one variation of a game our children play all the time. Other versions include, "Can't Catch Me Before I Get to My Bedroom," or "Can't Catch Me Before I Get to the Kitchen," or "Can't Catch Me Before I Get Outside."

I think our fifth-born Benjamin is the one who popularized this sport in our family. He's quick and agile and can turn on a dime, so he's pretty difficult to catch, even when multiple family members are giving chase.

There is really no other point to this game but to prove Ben wrong. That's the only objective.

We seldom succeed—Benjamin's younger sister Rachel is about the only one who can ever catch him—but we sure get a good workout trying!

# -85-
# Laser Maze

We tried something new this spring we'd never done before: We constructed our own "Laser Beam Maze." Using yellow yarn and blue painter's tape, we built a tangled, spider-web of a maze all down, about, and around our entry hall.

The finished project was about 20 feet of strings, a foot or so apart, running diagonally, horizontally, and crisscrossed, wall-to-wall and ceiling-to-floor. We then took turns trying to wiggle, squirm, jump, straddle, and crawl our way through—without touching any of the strings.

This was so much fun! We went littlest to biggest, and the staircase served as spectator stands for older siblings as they waited for their turns.

Of course, with as many boys as we have, everything turns into a competition, so we decided to time how long it took each child to navigate the maze, adding a 1-second penalty for every string touched on their way through. We started off with times as long as 35:58, but with repeated tries (and by jumping off the banister to bypass the first six or seven strings), the winner (our 20-year-old medical student who happened to be home on spring break) cut his time down to 8:57. That's pretty impressive, don't you think?

# -86-
# Simon Says

If you don't think "Simon Says" is a very challenging game, then you've obviously never played with the Flanders boys! They are *so tricky!* You can't just do what Simon does. You'll have to listen closely if you hope to survive. Here's how the typical game goes at our house:

"Simon says hop on one foot." Depending on how long they have to hop, some of our clumsier kids drop out here.

"Now switch!" Someone invariably does, and is also out.

"Simon says touch your ear!" But he says it while touching his nose and knocks out two more players who follow suit.

"Simon says to rub your tummy and pat your head." It's a complicated move, but most of us have this one down now.

"Now rub your head and pat your tummy." In our rush to prove we can make this change smoothly, we fail to notice Simon didn't issue that command. Three more get out.

"Simon says hold your breath." At Mom's insistence, "Simon says stop." But not until a couple of the more determined players have started turning purple…

# -87-
# Hide & Seek

Ready or not, here we come! You know how hide-n-seek normally calls for one person to hunt and everyone else to hide? Well, it's even more fun when only one person hides, and everybody else seeks!

When I was little, I was convinced my cousin Susan was the world's best at this game. She'd hide me in her bedroom—making her bed as if I were the pillows under the bedspread or hiding me in the drapes or on a shelf in the closet—then she'd call her brother Ricky to come and search. It always took him ages to find me, which I assumed at the time was because Susan was so clever about where she put me.

It wasn't until I had children of my own that I realized there might be another explanation—the one hinted at in Dorothy Aldis's wonderful poem, "I'm Hiding":

> *"I'm hiding, I'm hiding, and no one knows where;*
> *For all they can see is my toes and my hair."*

The father in the rhyme suggests places to hunt—in the inkwell, the mirror, under the carpet—but the mother fears she's lost her little son for good, until she spots his toes and hears him giggle. And I imagine it was my giggle that gave away my hiding places so many years ago, too.

# -88-
# Wiggle Rhymes

Taking a cue from children's librarians, we pause for a little stretch break when little ones get restless during read-aloud time. We'll sing or chant the following rhymes, complete with motions, before moving on to a new chapter:

*The grand old Duke of York* (hands on hips)
*He had ten thousand men* (point w/thumb over shoulder)
*He marched them to the top of a hill* (march in place)
*Then marched them down again* (squat down low)
*And when they were up, they were up* (reach up high)
*And when they were down, they were down* (squat low)
*But when they were only halfway up* (hunch over)
*They were neither up nor down.* (reach then squat fast)

This one's always been the favorite of my littlest ones:

*A funny fat frog, winking and blinking* (wink and blink)
*Looking so sleepy, sitting and thinking* (tap temple)
*Then... all of a sudden... he jumps!* (jump from a squat)

Stick your tongue out on all the *blaas* when singing this one:

*Blaaa-oop went the little green frog one day.*
*Blaaa-oop went the little green frog.*
*Blaaa-oop went the little green frog one day,*
*And it echoed back Oop-blaaaaaa!*

123

# -89-
# Circle Up

Games played in a circle are great for keeping children corralled in a semi-orderly fashion. Next time your kids need to run off energy in a confined space, try one of these:

- DUCK, DUCK, GOOSE: Players sit in a circle, while *The Goose* walks behind them, touching each head and saying, "Duck." If he says, "Goose" instead, that person must chase him around the circle and catch him before he sits down in the vacated spot. Otherwise, she becomes the new goose.

- DOGGIE, DOGGIE, WHERE'S YOUR BONE? Players sit in a circle with *The Doggie* in the middle. One person hides the "bone" (a rock or stick) behind his back while the Doggie's eyes are closed, then the Doggie tries to guess who has it. Once he does, that person becomes the Doggie and the game continues.

- QUIET WATER, STILL WATER: Mom calls out *"Quiet Water, Still Water, 1 2 3. See how quiet and still you can be."* She then watches to see who'll be first to move or make noise, and calls them out when they do. The quietest, stillest player left at the end of the game wins and gets to judge the next round.

Okay, so that last one isn't about burning off excess energy, but about giving Mom a break. Sometimes I need it!

124

Section 15

Spring
Training

# -90-
# Let's Go Fly a Kite

Kite flying isn't just for ingenious inventors with a key in a thunderstorm or for reformed workaholic fathers in *Mary Poppins.*

Children of all ages will enjoy tugging at the string of a kite, watching it dip and soar and reach for the clouds.

You can get a pretty decent kite without spending a lot of money. It's good to always keep one on hand, so you'll be ready when those breezy spring days that are so perfect for kite-flying present themselves.

Alternatively, you can visit your local craft store and get the supplies to make your own.

Whether you're flying a homemade kite or a store-bought, you'll want to take good care of it so that you'll be able to use it again and again. Fly it at the beach, in a field, or at a nearby park that has wide-open spaces.

Just make sure you stay away from the trees, or your kite-flying fun may be over in a hurry!

# -91-
# Easter Egg Hunt

My first brush with fame came when, at eight years old, I won the top prize at an Easter egg hunt in Heavener, Oklahoma, and got my picture in the town paper.

I was always extremely tall for my age and towered over the other children who were pictured with me. I suspect some of their mothers may have given my mother a dirty look for letting me hunt at all, but I was well within the specified age range to participate. I promise.

Thereafter, my Oklahoma cousins would always try to stump me by hiding eggs up in the trees branches, but I caught on fast and collected them all. The experience, however, ruined me for hunting in my hometown the following spring. Rather than actually hiding the eggs at that hunt, they simply scattered them in plain view, all over the ground. Unfortunately, I was so busy searching the trees that I didn't even notice and would've gone home empty-handed had another child not taken pity and shared her eggs with me. (Thanks, Kimberly—you're such a sweet sister!)

Our son Benjamin is the self-appointed Egg Hunt Officiate at our house. And I'm happy to report that he hides the eggs in such a way that it's a real challenge to find them. Which is as it *should* be, in my expert opinion. ☺

128

# -92-
# May Baskets

I love fresh flowers, don't you? My grandmother grew a garden full of flowers, and seldom did I visit her in the summertime that she didn't take me outside with a pair of scissors and let me pick out a nice bouquet.

I'd point out the varieties I wanted—roses, tiger lilies, purple coneflowers, and shasta daisies—and she'd cut the freshest blooms in the most inconspicuous way, so you could hardly tell anybody had been there, once we finished.

She'd tell me about how she and her friends used to fill small baskets with such fragrant blossoms, then leave them anonymously on one another's doorsteps the first day of May. They'd loop the basket's handle over the doorknob, then run off before they were discovered—an early version of Ding-Dong Ditching, but with a prize. Isn't that a lovely tradition?

Some years, the children have helped me make May baskets for our neighbors. Instead of filling them with flowers, we've filled them with candy treats or homemade goodies. We include a little note so they'll know who sent the gift, but we still try to sneak it onto the porch and dart away before they see it. That's half the fun!

# -93-
# So You Think
# You Can Dance?

One of our family's favorite ways to get our hearts pumping is by dancing. At home or away, dancing is great exercise.

Ballroom dancing. Line dancing. Salsa dancing. Break dancing. Irish step dancing. Polka. Swing. Tap and ballet. You name it, and we've probably tried it.

If you'd like to dance, but don't know how, look up some demonstration videos on YouTube or sign up for lessons at a local studio.

Doug and I and all our older children have taken a few semesters of ballroom dance—a fun way for homeschoolers to fulfill their physical education requirements.

Additionally, we all attend family-style dances several times a year, which provides a good opportunity for fellowship, as well as for keeping our *Virginia Reel* in good form.

# -94-
# Hula-Hoop
# Your Way to Health

Have you ever owned a hula-hoop? How long can you keep it going? Did you know there's a lot more you can do with a hula-hoop than twisting it around your waist? Why don't you drag yours out of the attic or basement and give one of these ideas a try:

- Spin the hula-hoop around your ankle, hopping over it with your other foot each time it flies past.
- Hang the hoop from a branch in a tree and take turns trying to toss beanbags through it.
- Holding the hoop at waist level, start flipping it over your head and under your feet, like jumping rope!
- Roll the hoop on its edge along the sidewalk. You may have to run to keep up. Don't let it fall!
- Fill a kiddie pool with homemade bubble solution (see Chapter 58) and use the hoop to make enormous bubbles. Stand in the pool, and you can be *in* one!

When you have the hoop revolving about your waist and it starts to fall, don't just give up and stop moving! Try to catch it around your knees and keep it spinning there by bending and flexing your legs. I once won a church-wide hula-hoop contest by doing this. *It's not over till it's over!*

131

# Section 16

Summer Sports

# -95-
# A Day at the Beach

We know lots of people probably can't imagine going all summer without a trip to the beach, but our family doesn't make it to the shore that often. And half the time when we do make it to the coast, it's off-season and sort of chilly. The upside of this? Our visits are all the more special for being so rare—and the beach is seldom crowded, so we have it to ourselves. That means more room to spread out and enjoy our favorite beachfront activities:

- BUILDING SANDCASTLES: Along with shovels and buckets, we tote sculpting tools for adding stone walls, chiseled arches, and wood grained doors.
- FLYING KITES: Just taking advantage of those wide, open spaces with no trees. (See Chapter 90).
- CHASING WAVES: Remember to pack life jackets for kids under six! Hold hands and stick together.
- FEEDING THE SEAGULLS: They like French fries (even the stale ones you find under your back seat).
- BURYING FAMILY MEMBERS: You can use your sculpting tools to add a mermaid tail afterward.
- HUNTING SEASHELLS: We enjoy searching, even if we've never found any souvenir-shop-worthy specimens. (That's why the shops are there… right?)

# -96-
# Pack a Picnic

No summer is complete without a least one good, old-fashioned picnic.

Fill a basket with fried chicken, pasta salad, cold watermelon, and fresh lemonade (but save the potato salad to eat at home… it's notorious for going bad when it goes unrefrigerated for more than an hour or two), then spread a quilt on the ground and eat under the trees.

During cooler months, our family has traditionally picnicked in the tree house that Dad and the boys built several years ago, or at the picnic table on our back porch.

In the summer, however, we take our dinner to the pool almost every night and eat it in the picnic pavilion there. Paper plates and cups makes cleanup super easy, and after an evening swim, the little ones don't even need baths before bed.

We return home and change straight into our bedclothes, then listen to Dad read bedtime stories before hitting the sack.

# -97-
# Cherry Pit Spitting

We love cherry season. Not only for the sweet, juicy cherries themselves, but also for the fun we have with all those pits!

At least once every summer, we stage a cherry pit-spitting contest. This is usually just a family affair, although we occasionally allow friends to join in the tradition.

We either divide the driveway into one-foot increments using a piece of sidewalk chalk or break out a measuring tape to check distances, but either way, we are always on the lookout for a new family record.

So far, nobody in our family has been able to best Dad's 1996 record of 39 feet, but when we staged a pit-spitting contest at a church fellowship a few years ago, one of our elders topped it with a distance of almost 50 feet. (If you ever manage to beat that, drop us a line and let us know!)

Participants must stay behind the start line to do their spitting, but we measure from that line to wherever the pit stops (including whatever distance it rolls).

Allergic to cherries? Try spitting (or pinching) watermelon seeds, instead.

# -98-
# Bicycle Parade

For many a year on the Fourth of July, our family hosted a neighborhood block party and bicycle parade.

Neighbors would come from up and down the block, across the street, and around the corner to celebrate America's independence with us. Our children usually biked around the neighborhood a week in advance, delivering invitations to every house. Each family was asked to bring their own lawn chairs, plus a 2-liter soda and a package of franks. We roasted the hotdogs on a gas grill in our driveway and provided paper goods, as well as chips, buns, condiments, and lots of ice-cold watermelon cut in thick, red slices.

The children decorated their bicycles with Americana signs, sparklers, streamers, and red, white, and blue balloons. Then after lunch, we would all parade around the block together. A contingent of vets would carry the flag to lead our procession. The children would follow riding their bespangled bikes, trikes, and wagons. And I'd usually bring up the rear, carrying a boom box playing John Phillips Sousa. Great marching music!

And great memories, as well!

# -99-
# Sand Volleyball

F lag football is not the only sport we play at family camp. We also compete in an annual volleyball tournament.

Camp rules dictate a girl must hit the ball during any play requiring more than one touch to get it over the net, which puts our boy-heavy clan at a bit of a disadvantage when we go up against a family with six (extremely athletic) daughters—but we have a wonderful time losing to them every year, anyway.

Last year, we wore tie-dyed Jamaican shirts as our team uniform. Anytime a teammate faulted, we encouraged each other by calling, "No worries, Mon!" This happened fairly frequently, since Rebekah, Rachel, and their woefully inexperienced mother were having to fill in for our older guys who'd recently moved away from home for medical and dental school.

We're determined to do better this year, but it's going to mean a lot of practice. Fortunately, the Sonics around here have sand volleyball courts attached. Does your Sonic have that, too? If you show up at ours during happy hour (daily from 3-5 for half-priced slushies), we may see you there and challenge you to a game!

# -100-
# Build a Fort

School's out. Weather's warm. Your children are looking for something to do. It's the perfect time to build a fort!

It doesn't have to be fancy. Just let them use whatever materials are handy:

- Chairs and blankets and couch cushions, too, can be fashioned into an amazing fortress in the eyes of a child. Give them a few safety pins or bag clamps for holding things together, so it won't accidentally collapse when they go to crawl inside.

- Cardboard boxes—appliance sized—make delightful forts. Give your kids as many of them as you can get your hands on, plus a roll of duct tape, and let their imaginations go wild. A parent or older child can add windows and doors with a box cutter, or if you're really brave, you can let them paint it.

- Wooden pallets, fallen branches, and scrap lumber can be twisted and woven together to make a little lean-to. Show your kids how to make a thatch roof with vines and pine straw.

Of course, if you want something more permanent, summer's a good time to work on building a tree fort, too. Talk to Dad about possibly making it a father/son project.

*Section 17*

Fall
Fitness

# -101-
# Leave the Leaves
# (for Now)

When it comes time for the leaves to fall, don't bag, burn, or mulch them immediately. Leave them long enough to have some family fun, first.

- Once your yard is completely covered with leaves, rake a maze of two-foot wide pathways through it, and then play a game of tag with your kids with the stipulation that all players must stick to the pathways. (Instead of "Don't Touch Ground" it becomes "Don't Touch Leaves.")

- After you've had your fun with the mazes, rake the leaves into a huge pile next to your swing set, then take turns jumping out of the swings and landing in the pile. (Play this only when the pile is fresh and bag them when you're through. Snakes and other critters will sometimes take refuge in a pile that has set for some time).

- Once you're ready to be rid of the leaves for good, have a contest to see who can fill the most bags the quickest. You can also use filled bags for building forts (see Chapter 100) and staging Nerf gun wars.

# -102-
# Corn Mazes
# & Pumpkin Patches

Every October, our homeschool group visits a local farm for a hayride, a lesson in agriculture, a pumpkin carving demonstration, and a trip through the pumpkin patch. My kids love this and look forward to going each year. Sometimes we even make two trips, once during the day to pick out our pumpkins, and once after dark, to try our skill at the corn maze.

If you ever get a chance to go through such a maze, you should try it. Be sure to bring a flashlight if you do, as it can be a little bit scary without one, even with a full moon.

If you have an incredibly good sense of direction, like my son Benjamin, you can navigate your way through the maze, no problem. (Then you can sit and wait and wonder what's taking the rest of your family so long.)

If, however, you were not born with a built-in GPS, you may want to try this failsafe method of finding your way through: Place your right hand on the OUTER wall as you enter the maze, then follow wherever it leads you. Just make sure you never take your hand off of that wall, and it will eventually bring you safely to the other side.

144

# -103-
# Trick-or-Treating
# (with a Twist)

We were able to avoid Halloween altogether for many years when our children were little. We'd turn out the lights, lock all the doors, and leave home, then spend the evening with friends celebrating Reformation Day, instead. We'd sing *A Mighty Fortress is Our God* and watch movies about Martin Luther's life. Those were the days!

But our approach to this holiday has changed with time. We now live in a neighborhood that happens to be a Halloween hotspot. Close to 1000 trick-or-treaters file onto our front porch every year to ask for candy, and we stay at home to give it to them. Along with all the Snickers and Skittles and Sour Patch Kids, however, we drop a little gospel tract into each of their pumpkin buckets. Some years we even distract the kids with magic tricks on the porch long enough to give some church friends time to share the gospel with their parents in the front yard.

If you want to start this tradition at your house, you'll find free printable tracts on our website (prescottpublishing.org). Pass them out at home, or take a stack with you if you're walking the neighborhood yourself and leave one at each house as a thank-you for the candy you're given.

# -104-
# Log Splitting
# & Wood Hauling

Shhh! Don't tell our boys that splitting logs is hard work. They think it's a big game.

Every fall when it's time to lay up firewood for the coming cold weather, we have no shortage of sons eager to prove their prowess with an axe. They strip off their shirts, flex their biceps, flaunt their abs, and set a timer, then chop like crazy to see who can split the most wood before the buzzer sounds.

One year for our son David's 16th birthday, we invited friends over and had a father-son log splitting contest. Entirely my husband's idea, it was the most popular party game we've ever played.

Since David's birthday is in February, our guys had finished splitting all our wood months earlier, so we had to borrow logs for the party from a neighbor (who was happy to get the job done for free).

The competition was stiff, but the fathers pulled ahead in the final seconds of the contest. Bigger beltlines bested bulging biceps in the end. ☺

# -105-
# Camping Out

Isn't it fun to sleep under the stars?

I have such fond memories of camping out with my parents and grandparents growing up, I wanted to give my own children the same experience. So every October, we pack up our gear, pitch our tents, and camp out for a full week in the Piney Woods of Big Sandy, Texas.

In that we always rent a campsite with running water and electricity, right across the road from the shower and restrooms, we can't rightly claim to be roughing it, but it's certainly a change of pace from the normal.

Even if you just pitch a tent in your own backyard, camping out can build great memories for you and your children.

Long before we began camping in state parks or *bona fide* campgrounds, we used to snuggle up in our little pup tent at home and listen to Dad read stories by lantern light. Even on cold nights, it always gave me a warm feeling inside to all be together in that way.

Section 18

Winter Workouts

# -106-
# Let It Snow!

Snow days make me happy. In the part of Texas where I grew up, snow days came few and far between—but, oh, how delightful they were when we got them!

The year I turned twelve, we got enough snow to actually go sledding. My daddy got up early that day and built a toboggan—*from scratch!* He lined the bottom with sheet metal, finished it before my sister and I even knew it had snowed, and presented it to us at breakfast.

As soon as our morning chores were finished, we all loaded into his truck, picked up a couple of our classmates, and headed to White Rock Lake where we spent the entire afternoon sledding down Flagpole Hill.

*Zoom!* That thing could *fly!* It was long enough that several children could ride on it at one time. I don't remember ever getting a better snow in all my childhood.

If you haven't the time or skill to build your own homemade sled next time it snows where you live, cookie sheets, large pieces of cardboard, skateboards with the wheels removed, and rain jackets will also work in a pinch. Just be sure to take a few turns down the hill along with your kids—to maximize the memory-making potential!

151

# -107-
# Do You Wanna
# Build a Snowman?

No mater how scant the amount of snow that falls, we feel compelled to build a friendly snowman if there is any accumulation at all, a practice that sometimes results in pathetically small snowmen.

I have a photo of all our little ones gathered proudly around a particularly squat two-footer one year. And it took almost all the snow they could find to build it *that* high.

Back in February of 2010, however, we got an amazing amount of snow (for this area, at least). It continued to fall for three or four days straight and our guys took full advantage of the opportunity to build a colossal snowman. It must have weighed as much as all our children put together.

It was nine feet tall and remained standing for weeks after the rest of the snow had melted, a testament to dogged determination, clever engineering, brute strength—and understanding neighbors. (The snowballs started in our yard, but ended up in theirs.)

Hint: If you ever decide to build a 9-footer yourself, you'll save some time (and your back!) by using a couple of 2x4's as ramps for rolling the mid-section and head atop the body.

# -108-
# Ice Skating

The lakes never freeze over down south, so we do all our ice skating at The Galleria in Dallas or Houston. We especially enjoy going in December, when the rink sports a ginormous Christmas tree, all bedecked with tinsel and twinkling lights.

We once skated at a rink (or *Eissportshalle*) in Germany that offered big rubber penguins with handles on their heads for children to push around on the ice for extra stability. Those things were terrific.

Here at home, there are no penguins, so we have our little ones stick close to the wall when they're first learning to skate—at least until a parent or older sibling is available to skate with them in the middle of the ice and hold their hand.

Once they are comfortable skating in a forward direction, we show them how to skate backward. My older kids are good at reversing direction on the go, but Mom and the little ones have to begin in a stationary position and move feet in an hourglass shape, first out, then in, then out again. If necessary, we push off from the wall to get going in the right direction.

Next time you strap a set of blades to your feet, give it a try!

153

# -109-
# Walking in a Winter Wonderland

Stepping out into fresh fallen snow is truly a breathtaking sight. The icy trees, the blanketed rooftops, the softly falling flakes floating gently to the ground in the crisp clean air—it is a magnificent thing to bear witness to all of this.

The first thing I do when such a day presents itself is to tiptoe out the backdoor and around to the front of the house (so as not to mar the front walk with footsteps) and snap a picture while it all looks so perfect. For I know that as soon as my children get up and dress, they'll come racing out the front door, and then it will be snowballs and snow boots and snow men and snow forts and tracks and scarves and mittens all over the porch and yard.

If Dad is home, he'll want us to take a walk before starting snowmen or staging snowball fights. He likes to walk first, so we can enjoy the beauty of all our neighbors' yards, before all our neighbors' kids get up and start doing at their houses what our children will shortly be doing at ours.

Once we return, the kids continue to play while Mom goes in and puts blankets in the dryer to warm their bodies and cocoa on the stovetop to warm their bellies one they come in from the cold. *Yum!*

# -110-
# Rudolph Run

The nice thing about running in the wintertime is that you don't work up quite as much of a sweat as in warmer weather. That's nice.

The bad thing is, you can feel like you're going to freeze before the starting whistle is ever blown. Brrrr!

One of the cool weather races our family has enjoyed running over the years is the Rudolph Family Fun Run held in Tyler the first of December. It's only a mile long, and there's no entry fee (although donations of cash or canned goods are encouraged), so our whole family can run without breaking the bank.

Our older kids have been known to register and run the 10K held immediately afterwards. The race benefits our local YMCA and, like the Turkey Trot, is a fun way to work in a workout during the holidays.

Lots of cities offer similar races: I've seen Jingle Bell Runs and Santa Runs and Ho Ho Runs and Reindeer Dashes. Check your Chamber of Commerce and find a race near you. Not only will it benefit charity, it will help burn off some of those calories you'll consume in Christmas candy!

155

# -111-
# Jingle Bells

One of our family's favorite Christmas traditions is bell-ringing for the Salvation Army. Every December (with the exception of the year we had the chicken pox), we pull out our Santa hats, bundle up warm, and head over to the mall to man the red kettle for an hour or two.

We usually sing Christmas carols as we ring, although the kids have occasionally brought a violin or a couple of harmonicas to play during our shift. The customers love it and are always very generous.

Some years, the weather has been bitter cold on the day we're scheduled to ring. That doesn't happen very often in Texas, but when it does, we don't want to keep our little ones out in it for a full hour, so we divide and conquer. Each child rings and sings with Mom for 10-15 minutes at a time, then spends the rest of the time inside the mall with Daddy or an older sibling, where they can get warm, buy a sweet treat, and knock out a little Christmas shopping.

Ringing the bell for Salvation Army this time of year makes a great family service project! They are always looking for fresh volunteers, and their new website makes it easy to help. Now you can sign up to ring bells online by visiting *www.ringbells.org.*

# - AFTERWORD -

Well, you made it to the end of the book! By now I hope you realize that fitness is about more than a trip to the gym, a number on the bathroom scale, or squeezing back into your skinny jeans (although those things may be fringe benefits).

Fitness is about being able to stay healthy and active for as long as we can. It's about taking care of the bodies God has given us, so that we can better serve Him and better care for our loved ones.

I hope what you've read will inspire you to *Get Up & Go!* If you incorporate just one of these suggestions into your schedule per week, you'll find enough ideas here to keep you busy for two full years!

That is more than enough time to establish lasting lifestyle changes and to build fitter, healthier bodies—all while making some fabulous memories that you and your children will treasure for years to come!

Where will your family's fitness journey take you? I'd love to hear about it when it happens! Send us a message through our publisher or connect with us online:

*www.flandersfamily.info*
*www.facebook.com/TheFlandersFamily*

May God's richest blessings be yours,

*Jennifer Flanders*

# - Coming Soon -
## from Prescott Publishing

From the Author of Love Your Husband/ Love Yourself

BALANCE

the
art
of
minding
what
matters
most

Jennifer Flanders

Introduction by Douglas R. Flanders, MD

BALANCE: the art of minding what matters most

# - MORE BOOKS -
## by Jennifer Flanders

*25 Ways to Communicate Respect to*
*Your Husband: A Handbook for Wives*

*Love Your Husband/ Love Yourself:*
*Embracing God's Purpose*
*for Passion in Marriage*

*Glad Tidings: The First 25 Years*
*of Flanders Family Christmas Letters*

*Balance: The Art of Minding*
*What Matters Most*
(coming in November 2014)

# - OTHER TITLES -
## from Prescott Publishing

### *100 Days of Blessing*
*(Volumes 1 & 2)*
by Nancy Campbell

### *Be ReVITALized:*
*Moments with Michelle*
by Michelle Kauenhofen

### *Cheer Up! Motivating Messages*
*for Each Day of the Year*
by Nancy Campbell and Michelle Kauenhofen

### *How to Encourage Your Husband:*
*Ideas to Revitalize Your Marriage*
by Nancy Campbell

### *How to Encourage Your Children:*
*Tools to Help You Raise Mighty Warriors for God*
by Nancy Campbell

# MORE GREAT BOOKS
## *from* PRESCOTT PUBLISHING

## The PRODIGY PROJECT

Someone is trying to resurrect ancient viruses hidden deep within the human genetic code to create a biological weapon so specific that it can target an individual...or an entire race. When two young prodigies discover their "medical research" is being used to build this weapon, they seek outside help to destroy it and to flee China.

Help comes in the unlikely guise of Jon Gunderson —doctor, bio-weapons expert, and devoted family man whose unsuspecting wife and nine children have unwittingly accompanied him on yet another assignment. Once the truth comes to light, the Gundersons will have to set aside their differences if they hope to rescue the prodigies and escape with their lives. The fate of the world hangs in the balance as the bittersweet dynamics of a large but loving family take center stage against the backdrop of China's breathtaking landscapes.

As the father of twelve home schooled children, author Doug Flanders is well acquainted with non-stop adventure. He draws on fifteen years experience as an Army Reservist and twenty years as a practicing physician to craft his fast-paced, family-friendly novels.

# GLAD TIDINGS

These refreshingly candid Christmas letters have been resonating with readers for 25 years. Now available for the first time in a single volume, together with collected quotes, favorite traditions, family recipes, and other assorted lists and ideas, Glad Tidings has something for everyone.

"I highly recommend this book. It shows the history of a family following God's will and call, and the blessings that followed!"
- Amazon reviewer M. McFarland

**Available at Amazon, Barnes & Nobles and fine bookstores everywhere or order through Prescott Publishing at http://prescottpublishing.org**

15479622R00100

Made in the USA
San Bernardino, CA
26 September 2014